Developing Numeracy
SOLVING PROBLEMS
ACTIVITIES FOR THE DAILY MATHS LESSON

year

3

Hilary Koll and Steve Mills

A & C BLACK

Contents

Reprinted 2001, 2002 (twice), 2003, 2004 (twice), 2005 (twice), 2007, 2008
Published 2000 by A & C Black Publishers Limited
38 Soho Square, London W1D 3HB
www.acblack.com
ISBN 978-0-7136-5446-2
Copyright text © Hilary Koll and Steve Mills, 2000
Copyright illustrations © Kirsty Wilson, 2000
Copyright cover illustration © Charlotte Hard, 2000
Editors: Lynne Williamson and Marie Lister
The authors and publishers would like to thank the following teachers for their advice in producing this series of books:
Stuart Anslow; Jane Beynon; Cathy Davey; Ann Flint; Shirley Gooch; Barbara Locke; Madeleine Madden; Helen Mason;
Fern Oliver; Jo Turpin.
A CIP catalogue record for this book is available from the British Library.
A & C Black uses paper produced with elemental chlorine-free pulp, harvested from managed sustainable forests.
Printed and bound in Great Britain by Cromwell Press Ltd, Trowbridge.

Introduction

Developing Numeracy: Solving Problems is a series of seven photocopiable activity books designed to be used during the daily maths lesson. They focus on the third strand of the National Numeracy Strategy *Framework for teaching mathematics*. The activities are intended to be used in the time allocated to pupil activities; they aim to reinforce the knowledge, understanding and skills taught during the main part of the lesson and to provide practice and consolidation of the objectives contained in the framework document.

Year 3 supports the teaching of mathematics by providing a series of activities which develop essential skills in solving mathematical problems. On the whole the activities are designed for children to work on independently, although this is not always possible and occasionally some children may need support.

Year 3 encourages children to

- choose and use appropriate operations to solve word problems and to use appropriate ways of calculating;
- solve mathematical problems and puzzles and to explore relationships and patterns;
- investigate a general statement about familiar numbers or shapes;
- explain their methods and reasoning;
- solve one-step and two-step worded problems in areas of 'real life', money and measures;
- recognise all coins and notes and understand the £.p notation.

Extension

Many of the activity sheets end with a challenge (**Now try this!**) which reinforces and extends the children's learning, and provides the teacher with the opportunity for assessment. On occasions you may wish to read out the instructions and explain the activity before the children begin working on it. The children may need to record their answers on a separate piece of paper.

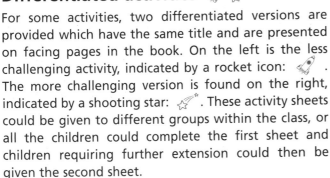

Differentiated activities

For some activities, two differentiated versions are provided which have the same title and are presented on facing pages in the book. On the left is the less challenging activity, indicated by a rocket icon: . The more challenging version is found on the right, indicated by a shooting star: . These activity sheets could be given to different groups within the class, or all the children could complete the first sheet and children requiring further extension could then be given the second sheet.

Organisation

Very little equipment is needed, but it will be useful to have available: coloured pencils, interlocking cubes, counters, scissors, coins, number lines, digit cards, real or plastic coins. You will need to provide 3-D shapes for page 29, paper shapes for page 35, and small clocks for pages 60–62, if desired.

Where calculators should be used, this is indicated on the page; otherwise it is left to the teacher's discretion.

To help teachers to select appropriate learning experiences for the children, the activities are grouped into sections within each book. However, the activities are not expected to be used in that order unless otherwise stated. The sheets are intended to support, rather than direct, the teacher's planning.

Some activities can be made easier or more challenging by masking and substituting some of the numbers. You may wish to re-use some pages by copying them onto card and laminating them, or by enlarging them onto A3 paper.

Teachers' notes

Very brief notes are provided at the foot of each page giving ideas and suggestions for maximising the effectiveness of the activity sheets. These can be masked before copying.

Structure of the daily maths lesson

The recommended structure of the daily maths lesson for Key Stage 2 is as follows:

Start to lesson, oral work, mental calculation	5–10 minutes
Main teaching and pupil activities *(the activities in the **Developing Numeracy** books are designed to be carried out in the time allocated to pupil activities)*	about 40 minutes
Plenary *(whole-class review and consolidation)*	about 10 minutes

Whole-class activities

The following activities provide some practical ideas which can be used to introduce or reinforce the main teaching part of the lesson.

Making decisions

Number puzzle

Address the whole class: *I have a number in my head, what could it be?* Ask the children to think of three questions to ask you about the number, for example: *Is it even? Is it more than six? Is it less than 14?*

Number question strip

On a strip of card or thick paper write a number fact, for example *17 + 24 = 41*. Wrap a narrow piece of paper around the strip of card so that it can slide sideways to mask one of the numbers or operator signs. Hold up the strip and ask the children to find the hidden number or sign. This can then be revealed to check that it is correct. You could build up a collection of number strips to use throughout the year.

Reasoning about numbers

Counting stick

You will need a stick which is divided into ten equal coloured sections (such as a metre stick with each 10 cm coloured). Hold the stick so that all the children can see it and point to each section along it in turn. Decide on a number (for example, two) and ask the children to count in twos as you point to each section. This provides practice in counting forwards and backwards and helps the children to remember the multiples of the given number. Odd and even numbers can be explored in this way, beginning with any odd or even number.

Double, double trouble

Choose a start number and then call out doubling and halving instructions, for example: *Begin with six. Double it, double it, halve it, double it. Which number are you on now?*

As a variation, you could give a range of addition, subtraction, multiplication or division instructions, for example: *Add three, multiply by two.*

Reasoning about shapes

Name the shape

a) Pick a shape from a bag of shapes and ask the children to name it and/or find its written name from some shape name cards.

b) Pick a shape but do not show it to the children. Describe it and ask the children to guess the shape name. They can ask three questions before guessing the shape, for example: *Does it have three sides?*

Problems involving 'real life'

Story world

Tell the children story questions involving simple calculations, for example:
My dog had four puppies. How many dogs do I have now?
Seven people were on a bus. Three more got on and one got off. How many are on the bus now?
I took twelve steps and then nine more. How many steps?
A hungry shark eats three sea horses, eleven fish and an octopus. How many things does the shark eat?
Ask the children to record the questions, using figures, and answer them.

Classroom quiz

Ask the children to estimate or count to answer classroom questions such as:
How many children are there in our class?
How many chairs are there?
Are there more chairs or children? How many more are there?
If we arranged the chairs into two rows, how many would be in each row?
If we arranged the chairs into groups of five (or ten), how many would be in each group?

Problems involving money

I started with…

Start by saying: *I started with £2 and bought something for 20p. Then I had £1.80 left.* Point to another child to continue: *I started with £1.80 and bought something for 30p. Then I had £1.50 left.* If correct, that child chooses another child to continue. Tell the children that they may not spend more than 40p at a time. When no money is left, start again at £2.

Problems involving measures

Classroom journeys

Ask the children to estimate the number of steps forward that a child should move from a marked spot in order to reach different objects in the classroom. Check the children's estimates and encourage them to respond to questions such as: *Is that far enough? Is it too far? How many more steps are needed?*

School fair

- ## Write a number statement for each number story.

1. There are 100 children and 200 adults at the school fair. 300 tickets are sold.

$$100 + 200 = 300$$

2. 6 children are on the bouncy castle. 2 more get on. 8 children are on the bouncy castle.

3. Jack has 50p and buys a packet of crisps for 22p. He gets 28p change.

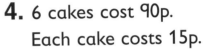

4. 6 cakes cost 90p. Each cake costs 15p.

5. You get 4 hoops each time you go on the Hoopla. Gemma has 3 goes. She gets 12 hoops.

6. A football team has 11 players. 5 football teams have 55 players.

- ## Make up four more number stories.
- ## Ask a partner to write the number statements using these signs.

| + | − | X | ÷ | = |

Teachers' note Different children may give different but correct number statements for the same number story, for example, the fourth story could be interpreted as 90p ÷ 6 = 15p or 6 x 15p = 90p.

Developing Numeracy
Solving Problems Year 3
© A & C Black 2000

Story teller

- **Write a number story for each number statement.**

1. $11 - 2 = 9$

There were 11 people playing
football and 2 got sent off.
Then there were 9.

2. $100 + 45 = 145$

3. $12 \times 5 = 60$

4. $20 \div 5 = 4$

5. $51 - 19 = 32$

6. $30 \div 3 = 10$

Now try this!

- **Write three different number stories
  for this statement.** $17 + 29 = 46$
  Use these words.

  total   more   altogether

Teachers' note This sheet can be used to create missing number statements by masking the instruction, worked example and one number in each statement, for example ☐ − 19 = 32. The statements can then be written as number questions, for example: 19 people got off a bus, leaving 32 people on the bus. How many people were on the bus at the start?

**Developing Numeracy
Solving Problems Year 3
© A & C Black 2000**

Magic cards

- **Use the cards to show how you would work out these questions.**

You can use a card more than once.

8 − 12 + 40 × 5 ÷ 4

1. A chair has 4 legs. How many legs do 5 chairs have?

5 × 4

2. There are 40 chairs arranged in 5 equal rows. How many chairs in each row?

3. My dad's ticket costs £8. Mine costs £5. How much do they cost altogether?

4. Max the magician has 12 scarves in each pocket. How many scarves in 4 pockets?

5. The show lasts 40 minutes. It stops after 12 minutes. How much longer does it have to go?

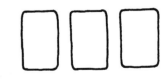

6. Max takes 12 rabbits from a hat. He puts them into 4 boxes with an equal number in each. How many rabbits in each box?

Now try this!

- **Now work out the answer to each question.**
- **Which was the most difficult to work out? Why?**

Teachers' note Children often try to use 'trigger' words (for example, 'left', 'take', 'altogether'), to help them decide which operation to choose, rather than trying to understand the situation. If children interpret question 6 as a subtraction, this may be because the word 'takes' is included and is incorrectly used as a trigger by them.

Developing Numeracy
Solving Problems Year 3
© A & C Black 2000

Computer bugs

Computer bugs have eaten all the signs.

- Fill in the missing signs to make each statement correct.

Use +, −, × or ÷.

1. 63 $\boxed{+}$ 98 = 161

2. 42 $\boxed{}$ 11 = 31

3. 101 $\boxed{}$ 75 = 26

4. 12 $\boxed{}$ 10 = 120

5. 14 $\boxed{}$ 2 = 28

6. 45 $\boxed{}$ 5 = 9

7. 87 $\boxed{}$ 48 = 135

8. 150 $\boxed{}$ 10 = 15

9. 172 $\boxed{}$ 97 = 75

10. 27 $\boxed{}$ 3 = 9

11. 120 $\boxed{}$ 60 = 60

12. 90 $\boxed{}$ 9 = 10

Now try this!

- **Make as many statements as you can using the numbers** $\boxed{4}$, $\boxed{2}$ **and** $\boxed{2}$.

Use the +, −, ×, ÷ and = signs.

Teachers' note Encourage the children to realise that, with whole numbers, the largest number in an addition and multiplication statement is the answer, and with subtraction and division, the largest number is the first number.

Developing Numeracy
Solving Problems Year 3
© A & C Black 2000

Lift the flap

Here is a 'lift the flap' book. Each flap hides a number.

• Fill in the hidden numbers.

1. 24 − 5 = 〔19〕

2. 8 × 2 = 〔 〕

3. 17 + 9 = 〔 〕

4. 14 ÷ 2 = 〔 〕

5. 18 + 〔 〕 = 27

6. 15 × 〔 〕 = 30

7. 25 ÷ 〔 〕 = 5

8. 65 − 〔 〕 = 54

9. 〔 〕 ÷ 2 = 9

10. 〔 〕 − 10 = 22

11. 〔 〕 × 10 = 40

12. 〔 〕 + 20 = 56

• **Check your answers using a different method.**

Now try this!

• **Use** 16 , 8 , 2 , ÷ **and** = **to make two more questions and answer them.**

Example: 8 ÷ 2 = 4

Teachers' note Use a number question strip (see page 5) to introduce the idea of missing numbers. Encourage the children to describe how they worked out each answer, drawing attention to those where a different operation from the one shown was used, for example: 'For 25 ÷ □ = 5, I knew that 5 x 5 was 25'.

Developing Numeracy
Solving Problems Year 3
© A & C Black 2000

- **Work out the answers. Show all your workings in the clouds.**

1. $27 + 58 =$

2. $146 + 37 =$

3. $83 - 49 =$

4. $152 - 63 =$

5. $17 \times 3 =$

6. $36 \times 2 =$

7. $40 \div 8 =$

Now try this!

- **Check your answers using a different method.**

Teachers' note The questions can be masked before photocopying to create a flexible resource. To create a simpler activity sheet write only addition questions, or a mixture of addition and subtraction questions, in the aircraft.

**Developing Numeracy
Solving Problems Year 3
© A & C Black 2000**

Which way?

- **Write the answers.**
- **Tick to show how you worked them out.** ✓

	in my head	using my fingers	using cubes	with pencil and paper	other way
1. $6 + 8 = 14$	✓				
2. $14 + 5 =$					
3. $7 + 19 =$					
4. $49 + 27 =$					
5. $142 + 86 =$					
6. $175 + 77 =$					
7. $13 - 4 =$					
8. $52 - 6 =$					
9. $64 - 37 =$					
10. $91 - 46 =$					
11. $158 - 70 =$					

- **Answer these questions.**

$27 - 9 =$	$46 + 17 =$
$50 + 180 =$	$275 - 10 =$

- **Which was the easiest to work out? Why?**

Teachers' note Encourage the children to discuss the extension activity in pairs or groups. Why do they think one question is easier than another? Is it because they have memorised the fact or can use their fingers quickly, or do they have a useful strategy for answering questions of this type?

**Developing Numeracy
Solving Problems Year 3
© A & C Black 2000**

Which way?

- **Write the answers.**
- **Tick to show how you worked them out.**

	in my head	using my fingers	using cubes	with pencil and paper	other way
1. 5 x 2 = 10	✓				
2. 7 x 5 =					
3. 4 x 3 =					
4. 6 x 4 =					
5. 15 x 3 =					
6. 18 x 2 =					
7. 12 ÷ 4 =					
8. 16 ÷ 2 =					
9. 15 ÷ 5 =					
10. 80 ÷ 10 =					
11. 25 ÷ 5 =					

Now try this!

- **Answer these questions.**

30 ÷ 5 =	21 x 2 =
90 ÷ 9 =	8 x 10 =

- **Which was the easiest to work out? Why?**

Teachers' note Encourage the children to discuss the extension activity in pairs or groups. Why do they think one question is easier than another? Is it because they have memorised the fact or can use their fingers quickly, or do they have a useful strategy for answering questions of this type?

**Developing Numeracy
Solving Problems Year 3
© A & C Black 2000**

Grid gremlins

The grid gremlins always move in a straight line.

1. Add three numbers in a straight line.

Do this in as many ways as you can.

Write the totals around the outside of the grid.

The line can be vertical, horizontal or diagonal.

4	2	5
5	1	3
6	3	2

2. What is the smallest total you can make? _____

3. What is the largest total you can make? _____

4. Write down the three numbers which add up to these totals:

9 __5__ __1__ __3__   10 _____

7 _____   12 _____

Now try this!

• **Now find four different ways to make a total of** 13 **. You can add any numbers that are touching.**

Example: 4 + 2 + 1 + 4 + 2 = 13

You can visit each number more than once.

Teachers' note Practise different techniques for adding several small numbers during the first part of the lesson. Encourage the children to record the number being added as well as the total, for example 5 + 4 + 1 + 3 = 13. This sheet can be used in conjunction with the next to provide differentiation in the main part of the lesson.

Developing Numeracy
Solving Problems Year 3
© A & C Black 2000

Grid gremlins

The grid gremlins always move in a straight line.

1. Add four numbers in a straight line.

Do this in as many ways as you can.

Write the totals around the outside of the grid.

12

4	5	1	6
2	4	3	3
1	6	5	7
4	6	8	2

12

The line can be vertical, horizontal, or diagonal.

2. What is the smallest total you can make? _____

3. What is the largest total you can make? _____

4. Write down the four numbers which add up to these totals:

16 _____   12 _____

18 _____   15 _____

19 _____   and _____

Now try this!

• **Now find four different ways to make a total of 24 . You can add any numbers that are touching.**

You can visit each number more than once.

Example: 6 + 5 + 7 + 3 + 3 = 24

Teachers' note Practise different techniques for adding several small numbers during the first part of the lesson. Encourage the children to record the number being added as well as the total, for example 5 + 4 + 1 + 3 = 13. This sheet can be used in conjunction with the previous one to provide differentiation in the main part of the lesson.

Developing Numeracy
Solving Problems Year 3
© A & C Black 2000

Digit patterns

- **Write the multiples in order, with the smallest at the bottom.**

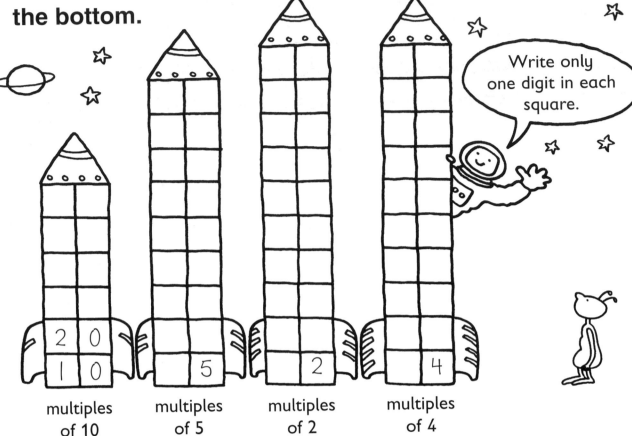

Write only one digit in each square.

2	0
1	0

multiples of 10

| | 5 |

multiples of 5

| | 2 |

multiples of 2

| | 4 |

multiples of 4

- **Look for a pattern in the units digits.**
- **Describe the pattern.**

Multiples of 10 _____

Multiples of 5 _____

Multiples of 2 _____

Multiples of 4 _____

Now try this!

- **Look at these doubling sequences.**

| 2, 4, 8, 16, 32, 64, 128… | 6, 12, 24, 48, 96, 192… |

- **Describe the patterns in the units digits.**
- **Use a calculator to continue the sequences and check the pattern.**

Teachers' note Begin this lesson with revision of multiples, for example by using a counting stick (see page 5). Encourage the children to describe the patterns they see to the rest of the class.

Developing Numeracy
Solving Problems Year 3
© A & C Black 2000

16

Special numbers

- **Use the special numbers above to make these totals. You can use each special number only once.**

	totals		totals
1	1		17
2	2		18
1 + 2	3		19
	4		20
	5		21
	6		22
	7		23
	8		24
	9		25
	10		26
	11		27
	12		28
	13		29
	14		30
	15		31
	16		

- **If you want to make totals beyond 31 , which will be the next special number?** _____

Teachers' note A doubling mental/oral starter such as 'Double, double trouble' (see page 5) might be useful to encourage the children to see the doubling nature of the special numbers used for this investigation.

Developing Numeracy Solving Problems Year 3 © A & C Black 2000

Odds and evens

Odd-Bod wants an $\boxed{\text{odd}}$ number of counters.

Even-Steven wants an $\boxed{\text{even}}$ number of counters.

Odd-Bod

Even-Steven

We must both have at least one counter.

- **Arrange seven counters in the trays so that each boy has what he wants.**

- **Record the different ways you can do this.**

  $1 + 6 = 7,$ _____

- **Now record the different ways you can do this with:**

  9 counters _____

  _____

  11 counters _____

  _____

  13 counters _____

  _____

Now try this!

- **Describe the patterns you can see.**
- **How many different ways for $\boxed{21}$ counters?**

Teachers' note Provide the children with counters to tackle this practically. Ensure that the children develop a systematic approach, for example, giving Odd-Bod one, then three, then five counters, etc. Encourage the children to describe the patterns they see to the rest of the class.

Developing Numeracy
Solving Problems Year 3
© A & C Black 2000

Odds and evens

Odd-Bod wants an **odd** number of counters.
Even-Steven wants an **even** number of counters.
Steady-Eddie doesn't mind how many he has.

Odd-Bod   **Even-Steven**   **Steady-Eddie**

We must each have at least one counter.

- **Arrange seven counters in the trays so that each boy has what he wants.**
- **Record the different ways you can do this.**

  1 + 2 + 4 = 7,

- **Now record the different ways you can do this with:**

  8 counters _____

  _____

  9 counters _____

  _____

  10 counters _____

  _____

  _____

Now try this!

- **Describe the patterns you can see.**
- **How many different ways for 11 counters?**

Teachers' note Provide the children with counters to tackle this practically. Ensure that the children develop a systematic approach, for example, giving Odd-Bod one, then three, then five counters, etc. Encourage the children to describe the patterns they see to the rest of the class.

Developing Numeracy
Solving Problems Year 3
© A & C Black 2000

19

Showtime game

- **Play this game in a group of three.**

☆ You each need three counters.
Hold your counters under the table.

☆ Put 3, 2, 1 or 0 counters in one hand and make a fist.
Don't let the others see!

☆ Put your fist on the table.

☆ Can you predict the **total** number of
counters that will be shown at Showtime?

Amy — I think 7.   **Jo** — I think 5.   **Kim** — I think 9.

☆ Say, 'Three, two, one, Showtime!'
and show your counters.

☆ Play the game ten times.
On the chart, record the results
for each game.

| 3 | 1 | 1 | total 5 |

Jo is the winner!

Number of counters			Total number of counters	Number of counters			Total number of counters
Player 1	Player 2	Player 3		Player 1	Player 2	Player 3	

Now try this!

- **Which totals come up more often than others?** _____

Teachers' note The Showtime game on this sheet can be used to provide a basis for the investigation on the following sheet. You may find it useful to discuss the game with the children before beginning, to ensure that each child understands the rules.

**Developing Numeracy
Solving Problems Year 3
© A & C Black 2000**

How to win at Showtime

Three children are playing Showtime.

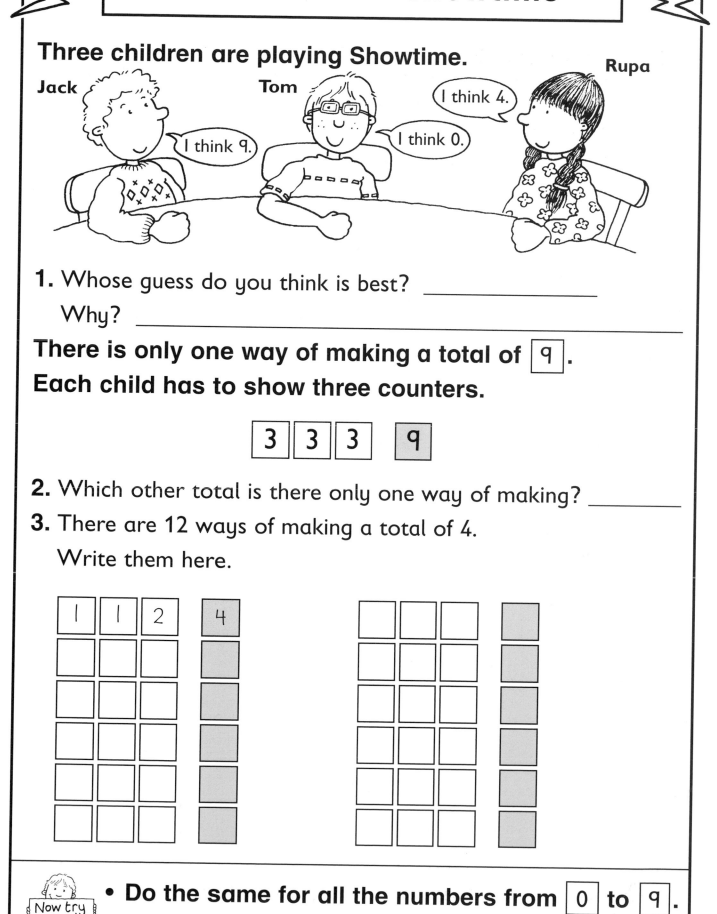

Jack — I think 9.

Tom — I think 0.

Rupa — I think 4.

1. Whose guess do you think is best? _____

Why? _____

There is only one way of making a total of 9 .

Each child has to show three counters.

| 3 | 3 | 3 | 9 |

2. Which other total is there only one way of making? _____

3. There are 12 ways of making a total of 4.

Write them here.

1	1	2	4

Now try this!

• **Do the same for all the numbers from** 0 **to** 9 .
How many ways can you find?

Teachers' note The children should play the Showtime game on the opposite page before tackling this sheet. Remind the class that in the game each child can only show 3, 2, 1 or 0 counters. Encourage them to work systematically and to see that there are fewer ways of making the totals 0, 1, 2, 7, 8, 9 than 3, 4, 5, 6. If desired, some children could work in pairs.

Developing Numeracy
Solving Problems Year 3
© A & C Black 2000

Chain letters

This capital letter is made from six squares.

The digits 1 to 6 are arranged in the squares.

The difference between the numbers in

touching squares is more than one.

1	3	6
	5	
	2	
	4	

- **Arrange the digits ☐1 to ☐6 in the letters below. The difference between the numbers in touching squares must be more than one.**

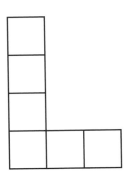
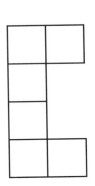
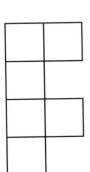
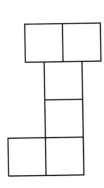

- **Arrange the digits ☐1 to ☐6 in the letters below. The total of each pair of touching numbers must be 7 or 8.**

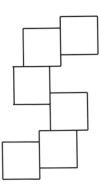
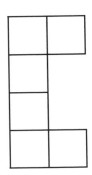
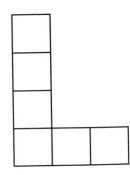
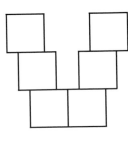

- **Is it possible to do both activities for this letter?**

Teachers' note Before beginning, revise the terms 'difference' and 'total' and ensure that the children are aware that they can use each digit only once. Note that diagonal squares are only relevant when part of their sides are touching, as in the letter 'S' above. The children can be given 1–6 digit cards to arrange in the same shape as the letter when tackling this activity.

**Developing Numeracy
Solving Problems Year 3
© A & C Black 2000**

Chain letters

This capital letter is made from nine squares. The digits 1 to 9 are arranged in the squares. The difference between the numbers in touching squares is more than one.

1	3	7
	5	
	2	
	4	
9	6	8

- **Arrange the digits 1 to 9 in the letters below. The difference between the numbers in touching squares must be more than one.**

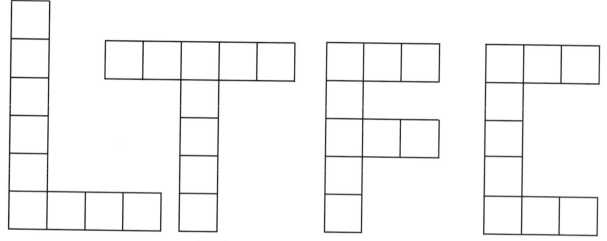

- **Arrange the digits 1 to 9 in the letters below. The total of each pair of touching numbers must be 9, 10 or 11.**

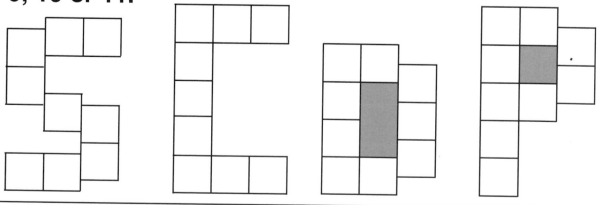

Now try this!

- **Is it possible to do both activities for this letter?**

Developing Numeracy
Solving Problems Year 3
© A & C Black 2000

23

Teachers' note Before beginning, revise the terms 'difference' and 'total' and ensure that the children are aware that they can use each digit only once. Note that diagonal squares are only relevant when part of their sides are touching, as in the letter 'S' above. The children can be given 1–9 digit cards to arrange in the same shape as the letter when tackling this activity.

Palindromic puzzles: 1

• **Look at this pattern. This is how you get from** 36 **to** 9 .

☆ Reverse the digits in 36.

☆ Take the smaller number from the larger number.

☆ Keep going until you reach 9.

☆ Count how many subtractions you have done.

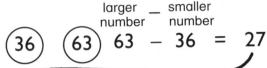
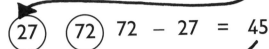
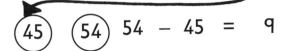

larger __ smaller
number   number

(36) (63) 63 − 36 = 27

(27) (72) 72 − 27 = 45

(45) (54) 54 − 45 = 9

The number 36 takes three subtractions to reach 9.

• **Follow the pattern for these start numbers until you reach** 9 .

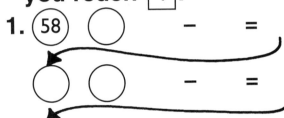

1. (58) ◯   −   =

   ◯ ◯   −   =

   ◯ ◯   −   =

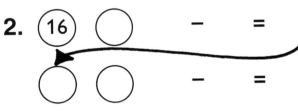

2. (16) ◯   −   =

   ◯ ◯   −   =

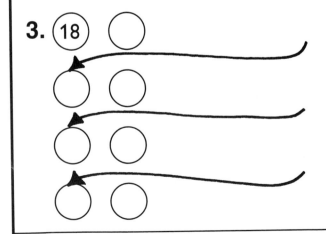

3. (18) ◯

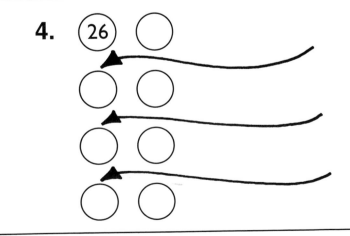

4. (26) ◯

Now try this!

• **What do you notice?**

• **Try other start numbers between** 12 **and** 50 .

Developing Numeracy
Solving Problems Year 3
© A & C Black 2000

Teachers' note Children use the following sheet to explore other start numbers in this way. Encourage the children to categorise start numbers into those that take 1, 2, 3, 4 or 5 subtractions to reach the number 9. Note that numbers such as 11, 22, 33, 44, etc. cannot be used for this investigation. Ensure that the children understand what a palindrome is.

• **Draw a ring around each set when you reach** $\boxed{9}$ **.**

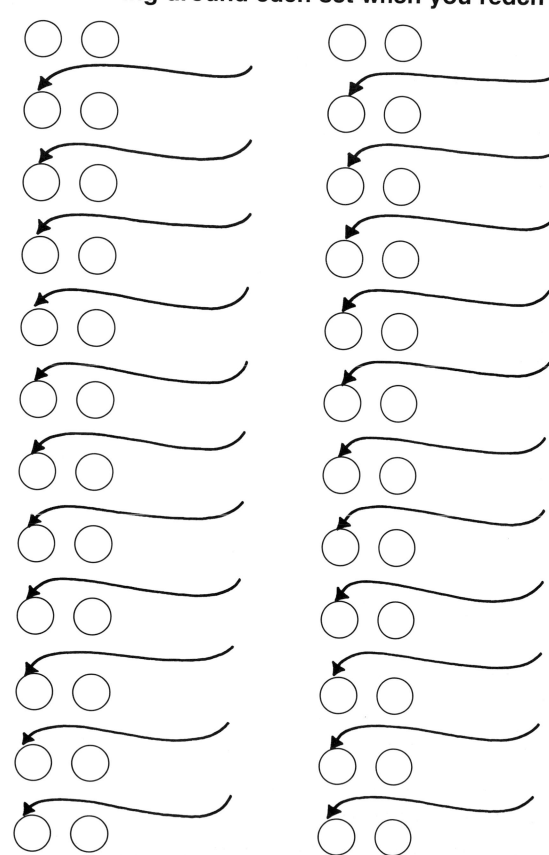

Teachers' note This sheet should be used to provide children with a structure for investigating 'Palindromic puzzles' on the previous sheet.

Developing Numeracy
Solving Problems Year 3
© A & C Black 2000

Number cruncher

The number cruncher has made up some statements.

- Tick to show whether each statement is ☐true☐ or ☐false☐.
- Write four examples to prove this.

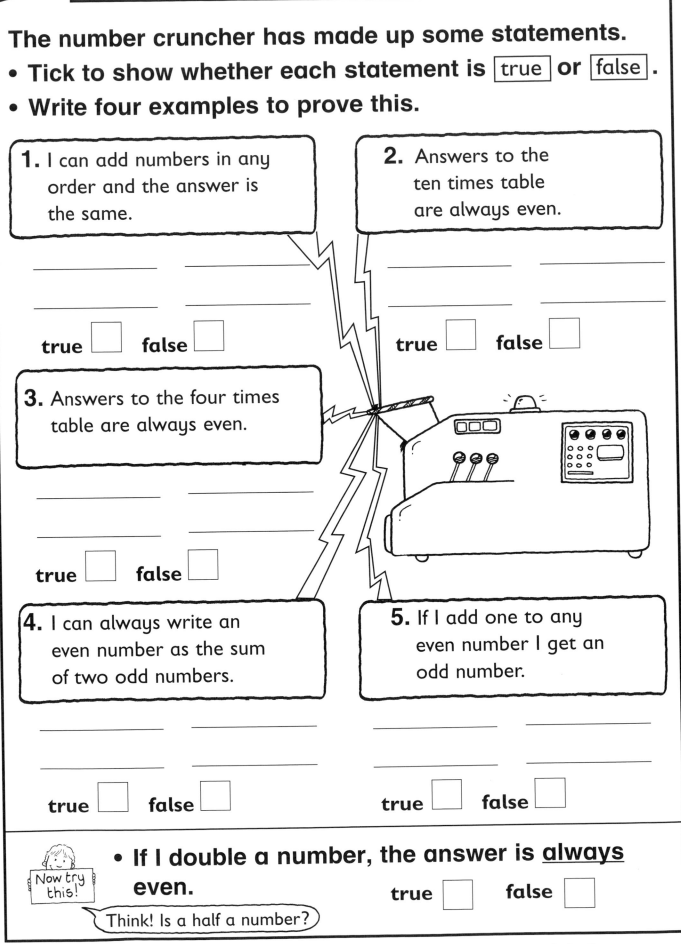

1. I can add numbers in any order and the answer is the same.

_____

_____

true ☐   false ☐

2. Answers to the ten times table are always even.

_____

_____

true ☐   false ☐

3. Answers to the four times table are always even.

_____

_____

true ☐   false ☐

4. I can always write an even number as the sum of two odd numbers.

_____

_____

true ☐   false ☐

5. If I add one to any even number I get an odd number.

_____

_____

true ☐   false ☐

Now try this!

- **If I double a number, the answer is _always_ even.**   true ☐   false ☐

Think! Is a half a number?

Teachers' note Discuss the extension activity with the class at the end of the lesson and draw attention to the need to be exact when making statements like this, for example by using the word 'whole' to describe the numbers. Ensure that the children realise that giving one example is insufficient to prove a general statement, although one example can be enough to disprove it.

Developing Numeracy
Solving Problems Year 3
© A & C Black 2000

Who is right?

Odd-Bod and Even-Steven are arguing.
- **Tick the right answer.**
- **Write four examples to prove this.**

1. Double a whole number and add one. The answer is always…

☐ …an odd number. …an even number. ☐

_____
_____
_____
_____

2. If you add one to any odd number you get…

☐ …an odd number. …an even number. ☐

_____
_____
_____
_____

3. If you add an odd number to an odd number you get…

☐ …an odd number. …an even number. ☐

_____
_____
_____
_____

4. If you add two to any even number you get…

☐ …an odd number. …an even number. ☐

_____
_____
_____
_____

- **Halve an even number and you will <u>always</u> get an odd number.** true ☐ false ☐

Teachers' note Discuss the extension activity with the class at the end of the lesson and encourage the children to create their own true/false statements of this type. Ensure that the children realise that giving one example is insufficient to prove a general statement, although one example can be enough to disprove it.

**Developing Numeracy
Solving Problems Year 3
© A & C Black 2000**

Happy hedgehog

Look at this plan of a garden.
A hedgehog wants to eat all the
slugs and then go home!

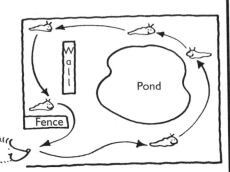

- On each plan use arrows to draw a
  different route for the hedgehog.

1.

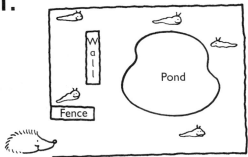

2.

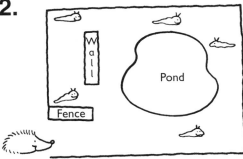

3.

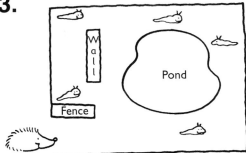

4.

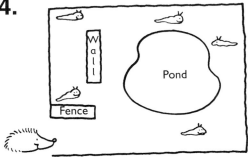

On this plan the slugs are marked with letters.

- Use the letters to show the order in which the
  hedgehog could eat the slugs.

Example: A B C D E

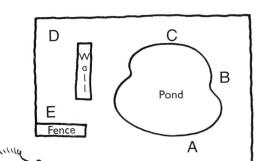

- Write all the different ways
  you can find.

Teachers' note Discuss with the children that the hedgehog is unable to cross the pond, or climb the fence or wall. The children could draw maps of their own for a partner to find the different routes.

**Developing Numeracy
Solving Problems Year 3
© A & C Black 2000**

Planet of the shapes

All shapes on the planet Zog have an even number of faces .

Which of these shapes might you find on Zog?

- Write how many faces each shape has.
- Colour the shapes with an even number of faces.

cube ___   sphere ___   cylinder ___   square-based ___
pyramid

 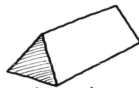  

cone ___   triangular ___   cuboid ___   hemisphere ___
prism

To enter Zog you need shapes with a total of 24 faces.

- Using the coloured shapes, find different ways of making a total of 24 faces.

4 cubes

1 cone and 11 hemispheres

- Find different ways of making a total of 26 faces.

Teachers' note Encourage the children to think of as many different ways as they can. Ensure that the children understand the meaning of the word 'face' and provide 3-D shapes so that the children can count the faces.

Developing Numeracy Solving Problems Year 3 © A & C Black 2000

Hopping mad: 1

The frog wants to hop across the lilypads to eat the fly.
He can only hop to a lilypad next to the one he is on.

Here the frog hops 7 times to reach the fly.

Here is another '7 hop' route.

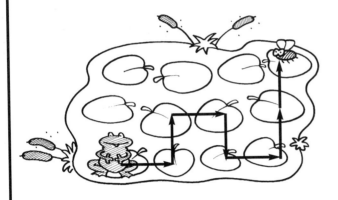

1. Draw and label some more '7 hop' routes.

2. Draw and label as many '5 hop' routes as you can.

3. Now draw and label some '6 hop' routes.

4. Now draw and label some '4 hop' routes.

5. The frog is hungry. It wants to reach the fly quickly!
Draw and label the shortest route it can take.

6. Show how the frog can reach the fly if it hops onto each pad once.

• **Find different ways for the frog to visit each pad once.**

Teachers' note The children will need copies of the 'Hopping mad' sheet on the opposite page to record their answers. Explain to the children that the frog can jump vertically, horizontally and diagonally to any adjacent pad. Discuss their answers as a whole class and then encourage the children to compare routes with a partner.

Developing Numeracy
Solving Problems Year 3
© A & C Black 2000

Hopping mad: 2

Teachers' note The children should use this sheet to record their answers for the previous page. Some children may require more than one of these sheets. Suggest that they use a pencil and rubber to try out their routes first. They could use different colours to mark more than one route on the same plan. Encourage the children to label each route they draw.

**Developing Numeracy
Solving Problems Year 3**
© A & C Black 2000

Shape up!

Here are two identical triangles.
You can join them to make different shapes.

rectangle   quadrilaterals   triangles   pentagon   hexagon

- **Cut out the rectangles at the bottom of this sheet.**
- **Arrange them to make the shapes on the chart. The rectangles must not overlap.**
- **Draw the shapes.**

1. a square	**2.** a rectangle
3. a hexagon	**4.** an octagon
5. a different octagon	**6.** a different octagon

Teachers' note Before beginning this activity, discuss the properties of 2-D shapes with the children and play 'Name the shape' (see page 5). Remind the children that the rectangles must be joined along one side. When counting the sides of the new shapes they have made, the children may make the mistake of counting lines within the shape rather than just around the edge.

Developing Numeracy
Solving Problems Year 3
© A & C Black 2000

Shape up!

Here are two identical triangles.
You can join them to make different shapes.

 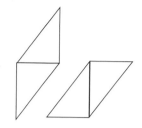 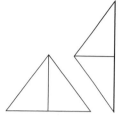 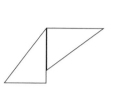

rectangle   quadrilaterals   triangles   pentagon   hexagon

- **Cut out the quadrilaterals at the bottom of this sheet.**
- **Arrange them to make the shapes on the chart. The quadrilaterals must not overlap.**
- **Draw the shapes.**

1. a hexagon	**2.** a different hexagon
3. a different hexagon	**4.** an octagon
5. a different octagon	**6.** a quadrilateral

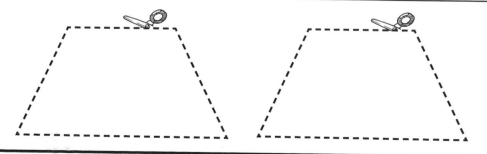

Teachers' note Discuss the properties of the 2-D shapes on the chart before beginning this activity. Remind the children that the quadrilaterals must be joined along one side. When counting the sides of the new shapes they have made, the children may make the mistake of counting lines within the shape rather than just around the edge.

**Developing Numeracy
Solving Problems Year 3
© A & C Black 2000**

True or false?

- **Tick to show whether each statement is** [true] **or** [false] .
- **Draw and label some examples to prove this.**

A flat shape with four corners and four straight sides is always called a rectangle.

not a rectangle

not a rectangle

a rectangle

true [ ] **false** [✓]

A flat shape with three corners and three straight sides is always called a quadrilateral.

true [ ] **false** [ ]

A flat shape with eight corners and eight straight sides is always called an octagon.

true [ ] **false** [ ]

A flat shape with five corners and five straight sides is always called a hexagon.

true [ ] **false** [ ]

Now try this!

- **Write three true statements about flat shapes for a partner to check.**

Teachers' note In the extension activity, ask the children to test each other's statements to check whether they are true. Remind them of the importance of giving more than one example when checking.

Developing Numeracy
Solving Problems Year 3
© A & C Black 2000

Paper folding

- **Fold paper shapes to find out which answer is correct.**
- **Draw the shapes you make.**

Sometimes both answers might be correct!

1. Fold a square in half.

Which shapes can you make?

rectangle ☑   **triangle** ☑

2. Fold a circle in half.

Which shapes can you make?

sphere ☐   **semi-circle** ☐

3. Fold a triangle in half.

Which shapes can you make?

triangle ☐   **rectangle** ☐

4. Fold an octagon in half.

Which shapes can you make?

pentagon ☐   **hexagon** ☐

5. Fold a hexagon in half.

Which shapes can you make?

quadrilateral ☐   **triangle** ☐

Now try this!

- **Fold a rectangle in half. Which shapes can you make?**
- **Try it for different rectangles.**

Teachers' note Provide the children with paper shapes for this activity. Encourage them to test irregular shapes as well as regular ones.

**Developing Numeracy
Solving Problems Year 3**
© A & C Black 2000

Class quiz

- **Find out the answers for your class and complete the chart.**

1. The number of children in our class today [ ]

   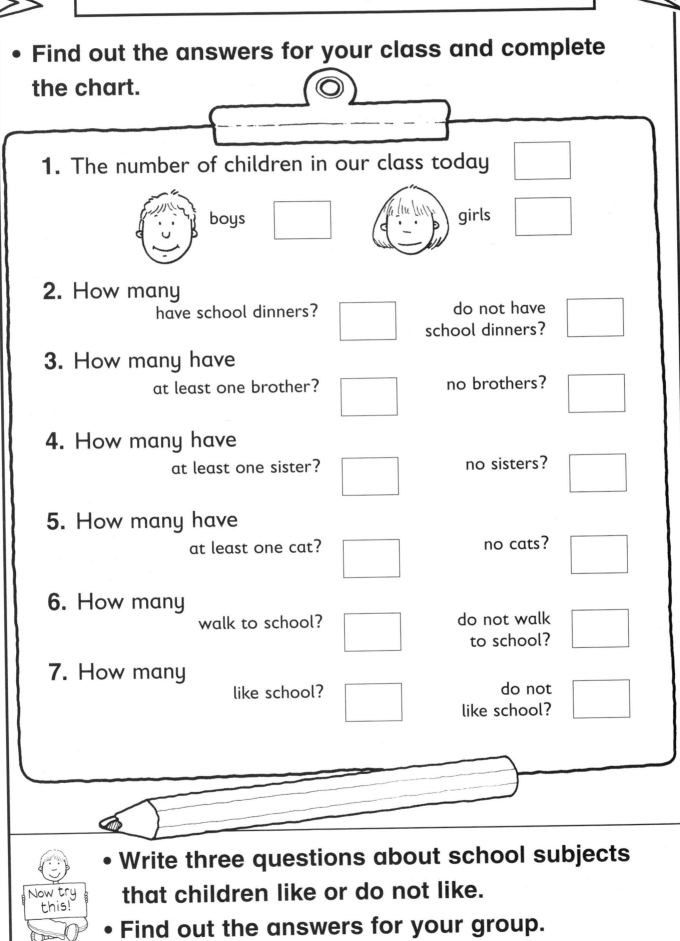 boys [ ]   girls [ ]

2. How many
   have school dinners? [ ]   do not have school dinners? [ ]

3. How many have
   at least one brother? [ ]   no brothers? [ ]

4. How many have
   at least one sister? [ ]   no sisters? [ ]

5. How many have
   at least one cat? [ ]   no cats? [ ]

6. How many
   walk to school? [ ]   do not walk to school? [ ]

7. How many
   like school? [ ]   do not like school? [ ]

- **Write three questions about school subjects that children like or do not like.**
- **Find out the answers for your group.**

Teachers' note This sheet can be partially completed as a whole class, where the first column of the sheet is filled in as the children put up their hands. The children, individually or in pairs, can then work out the missing numbers in the second column.

Developing Numeracy
Solving Problems Year 3
© A & C Black 2000

Gardeners' world

- **Solve these number problems.**

1. 16 worms are on the lawn. The birds eat 7. How many worms are there now? ▢

2. 9 bulbs are in the border. I plant 8 more. How many bulbs are there now? ▢

3. There are 21 cabbages. The slugs eat 6. How many cabbages are there now? ▢

4. 15 bees are on the flowers. 13 more arrive. How many bees are there now? ▢

5. 18 ants are marching in a line. 7 leave. How many ants are there now? ▢

6. 12 birds land on the bird table. There are now 21 birds there. How many birds were already on the table? ▢

- **Write two different number stories to show how there could be ▢29 birds on the table.**

Teachers' note Children often look for 'trigger' words, like 'times', 'altogether' or 'share', to help them solve problems. If triggers are always included in worded problems children can avoid much of the necessary thinking process.

Developing Numeracy
Solving Problems Year 3
© A & C Black 2000

Pinball wizard

You are playing pinball. You score points when the ball hits a pad .

• **Fill in your score.**

1.

2.
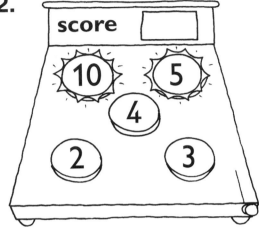

3.

4.

5. You score 12, then you hit the ⟨5⟩ pad.

What is your score? _____

The ball can hit a pad more than once.

6. How can you score 16? _____

7. How can you score 20? _____

8. How can you score 27? _____

  • **Show two ways you can score** 30 .

Teachers' note Encourage the children to consider multiplication as well as addition when finding ways of scoring 16, 20 and 30. They could be asked to list as many different ways of finding 20 as they can.

**Developing Numeracy
Solving Problems Year 3**
© A & C Black 2000

Pinball wizard

You are playing pinball. You score points when the ball hits a pad .

• **Fill in your score.**

1.

2.

3.

4.

5. You score 19, then you hit the (10) pad.

What is your score? _____

6. You score 17, then you hit the (4) pad and the (5) pad.

What is your score? _____

> The ball can hit a pad more than once.

7. How can you score 32? _____

8. How can you score 39? _____

Now try this!

• **Show three ways you can score** 45 .

Teachers' note Encourage the children to consider multiplication as well as addition when finding ways of scoring 32 and 45. They could be asked to list as many different ways of finding 32 as they can.

Developing Numeracy
Solving Problems Year 3
© A & C Black 2000

Classroom chaos

• **Colour the tables which have correct statements.**

1. There are 15 rulers and 16 pens on the table. There are 31 things on the table.

2. The teacher has 13 books and 28 pencils. He has twice as many pencils as books.

3. Pencils come in boxes of 4. The teacher opens 7 boxes to get 28 pencils.

4. There are 6 children at each table. There are 5 full tables. There are 30 children in our class.

5. Today there are 28 children in the class. The teacher has 56 sweets. She can give 2 sweets to each child.

6. There are 10 books on a table. There are three times as many pens. There are 30 pens on the table.

7. In the teacher's desk are 31 pins. She uses some to pin up pictures. There are 16 left, so she used 17 pins.

• **Write the number statement you used to solve each question.**

Example: 15 + 16 = 31

Teachers' note Encourage the children to model each situation with real objects if necessary.

Developing Numeracy
Solving Problems Year 3
© A & C Black 2000

Parking problems

- **Solve these number problems.**

1. 19 cars are in the car park. 18 more arrive.
How many cars are there now? ☐

2. 34 cars are in the car park.
15 more arrive. How many
cars are there now? ☐

3. 27 cars are in the car park. 7 leave but 15 more arrive.
How many cars are there now? ☐

4. The car park has 2 floors. 26 cars can fit on each
floor. How many cars can fit in the car park? ☐

5. If there are 6 empty spaces on each floor, how many
cars are in the car park? ☐

18 **cars arrive in the car park.**

- **There are 2 people in each car. How many
people arrive?** ☐
- **Each car has 4 seats. How many seats
are there in total?** ☐

Teachers' note Children often look for 'trigger' words, like 'times', 'altogether' or 'share', to help
them solve problems. If triggers are always included in worded problems children can avoid much
of the necessary thinking process.

**Developing Numeracy
Solving Problems Year 3
© A & C Black 2000**

The fruit shop

On a shelf in the fruit shop there are:

| 10 peaches | 27 apples | 16 oranges |

1. In total there are _____ pieces of fruit.

2. I would like 11 oranges please.

That leaves _____ pieces of fruit.

3. The apples are in boxes of 5. There are _____ full boxes.

4. On another shelf there are 6 bananas. Next to them are 5 times as many grapes. That makes _____ grapes.

5. I shall divide the grapes equally into 3 bags. That means putting _____ grapes into each bag.

6. There are _____ more grapes than bananas.

Now try this!

There are | 5 plums | **and** | 5 pears | .

• **Write the different ways you can have 6 pieces of fruit.**

Example:	plums	pears	pieces of fruit
	1	5	6

Teachers' note In the extension activity the children may need help to be systematic when exploring ways of finding six pieces of fruit. Further totals can be set with a third fruit added.

Developing Numeracy
Solving Problems Year 3
© A & C Black 2000

At the supermarket

- **Solve these problems.**

1.

I want 31 baking potatoes.
A bag holds 5 potatoes so
I shall need _____ bags.
_____ bags will be full.

2. Tins of cat food come in
packs of 4. I need 26 tins
so I buy _____ full packs.

3. I stack 4 shelves with 8 loaves
on each shelf. There are _____
loaves on the shelves.

4.

There are 40 magazines and 5 racks.
I put an equal number of magazines on
each rack. There are _____ magazines
on each rack.

5. I have 2 piles of tins. There are 23 tins in one
pile and 38 in the other pile. If I put the tins
in boxes of 6, I will need _____ boxes.

- **Write the different ways you can put 6 tins into 3 piles.**

Example:	pile 1	pile 2	pile 3
	4	1	1

Teachers' note The extension activity is designed to encourage the children to be systematic in their thinking and recording. Different quantities and numbers of piles can be explored in a similar way. Other contexts can be used, such as cubes into bags and rabbits into pens.

Developing Numeracy
Solving Problems Year 3
© A & C Black 2000

Spend, spend, spend!

- **Solve these money problems.**

1. How many £1 coins can you swap for a £5 note? _____

2. You pay for the items on the chart with a £5 note.

Complete the chart. Draw the coins used for change.

Item	Cost	Change from £5	Coins used for change
1 scarf	£1.50	£3.50	£1 £1 £1 50p
1 cap			
5 pens			
1 comic and 1 yo-yo			

3. If you save 50p a week, how many weeks will it take

you to save £5? _____

4. If you want to buy a T-shirt for £8.60, how much more

than £5 do you need? _____

- **You buy any three things and spend exactly £5 . What could the things have cost?**

Teachers' note The children may need the support of real or plastic coins. In the extension activity, encourage the children to explore different ways of spending exactly £5 on three items. They should record their work to help them spot patterns. Encourage them to realise that if the price of one item is raised, another must be reduced by the same amount.

Developing Numeracy
Solving Problems Year 3
© A & C Black 2000

Spend, spend, spend!

£6.50 £8.65 £7.80 £1.25

• **Solve these money problems.**

1. How many 50p coins can you swap for a £10 note? _____

2. You pay for the items on the chart with a £10 note.
Complete the chart. Draw the coins used for change.

Item	Cost	Change from £10	Coins used for change
1 football			
1 video			
1 card and 1 book			

3. If you want to buy a jacket for £17.05, how much more than £10 do you need? _____

4. Jo saves £1.40 each week. She started five weeks ago. How much has she saved? _____

5. Sam has £10. He is given £3.50 but he spends £5.30. How much does he have now? _____

Big Dipper 60p   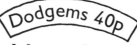 Dodgems 40p

• **If Ali goes on each ride at least once and spends exactly £2.40 , how many times does he go on each ride?**

Teachers' note As a further extension, encourage the children to find as many different ways as they can of spending exactly £2.80 on the rides. They should record their work to encourage them to be systematic and can check their results with a partner.

Developing Numeracy
Solving Problems Year 3
© A & C Black 2000

- **Solve these money problems. You can use the same coin more than once.**

1. Write three different ways to pay **60p**.

20p 20p 20p

50p 10p

10p 10p 10p 10p 10p 10p

2. Write three different ways to pay **72p**.

_____

_____

_____

3. Write three different ways to pay **£1.02**.

_____

_____

_____

4. Write three different ways to pay **£2.20**.

_____

_____

_____

5. How can you pay **29p** with four coins?

_____

6. How can you pay **97p** with five coins?

_____

- **Write how you would pay these amounts. Use as few coins as you can.** | 46p | £2.98 |

Teachers' note Some children may need the support of real or plastic coins for this activity. Shop role-play can be used to act out similar situations.

Developing Numeracy
Solving Problems Year 3
© A & C Black 2000

Code-crackers

This code gives a value to each letter.

a	b	c	d	e	f	g	h	i	j	k	l	m	n
1p	2p	3p	4p	5p	6p	7p	8p	9p	10p	11p	12p	13p	14p

o	p	q	r	s	t	u	v	w	x	y	z
15p	16p	17p	18p	19p	20p	21p	22p	23p	24p	25p	26p

● **Find:**

the name of a colour and its value	b l u e 2p + 12p + 21p + 5p = 40p
a colour with a low value	
a colour with a high value	
a pet worth 26p	
a girl's name worth less than 50p	
a boy's name worth between 50p and £1	
a three-letter word with a value of 10p	

● **Write down words with high values which have** [two letters] , [three letters] , [four letters] **and** [five letters] .

Now try this!

Teachers' note The children should be encouraged to concentrate on different parts of the alphabet if they are trying to make low- or high-value words. Encourage them to record the related number statements as well as the words. The children could make up more questions for a partner to solve. They might also like to find the values of their own names.

Developing Numeracy
Solving Problems Year 3
© A & C Black 2000

Eating out

Kirsty and her friends go to the Big Bite.

• **Work out the bills.**

Pizza £2.45

Salad £1.10

Fries £0.80

Burger £1.35

Milkshake £0.75

Cola £1.00

1. Leela has a pizza and a milkshake. What does her meal cost?

_____

2. Kirsty has fries, a burger and a cola. How much does this cost?

_____

3. Liam spends £1.55. What does he have?

_____

4. Emma's meal costs £2.90. What does she have?

_____

_____

_____

5. Jack spends £2.45. Which two different meals might he have?

Meal 1 _____

Meal 2 _____

Now try this!

Zoe takes £3.50 to the Big Bite.

• **What different meals can she afford to buy?**

• **What change would she get from each one?**

Teachers' note As a mental/oral starter to this activity, you could play 'I started with' (see page 5) with the children. In the extension activity, the children should be encouraged to find as many different meals as they can. Other sums of money to be spent can be introduced as appropriate.

Developing Numeracy Solving Problems Year 3 © A & C Black 2000

Fairground fun

Log Flume £2.00

Candy floss 45p

Toffee apple 65p

Helter Skelter £1.50

Ghost Train £3.00

Big Wheel £2.00

• Solve these problems for Leah and Ian.

1. I go on the Big Wheel, the Log Flume and the Ghost Train. The total cost is _____ .

2. The Ghost Train costs _____ more than the Big Wheel.

3. I spend £4.50 on two rides. I go on the _____ and the _____ .

4. I go on the Big Wheel and buy a candy floss. I spend _____ altogether.

5. I buy three candy flosses. I spend _____ altogether.

6. I spend _____ on two toffee apples.

• Each child has £5 left. How many more:

candy flosses can Leah buy? _____

toffee apples can Ian buy? _____

Now try this!

Teachers' note Ensure that the children are familiar with vocabulary such as 'total', 'altogether', 'more', etc.

Developing Numeracy
Solving Problems Year 3
© A & C Black 2000

Crazy golf

- **Look at the prices for the crazy golf course.**

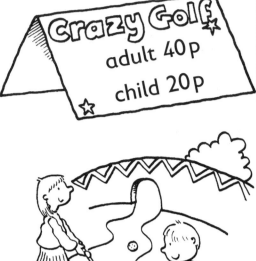

Crazy Golf
adult 40p
child 20p

1. Complete the chart.

Players	Cost
2 adults	
5 children	
10 children	
1 adult and 1 child	
2 adults and 2 children	
5 adults and 4 children	

2. Who can play for 80p? _____ **or**

_____ **or** _____

3. Who can play for £1? _____ **or**

_____ **or** _____

4. Which costs more, 4 adults or 10 children? _____

Now try this!

- **Change the prices so that it costs the same for** ⬚2 adults⬚ **or** ⬚5 children⬚. **Write the new prices on this sign.**
- **Using the new prices, make up two questions for a partner to answer.**

Crazy Golf
adult ____ P
child ____ P

Teachers' note The prices could be masked and different prices and totals added to provide a flexible resource. In the extension activity, encourage the children to begin with trial and error strategies to gain an initial idea of approximately what the new prices could be.

Developing Numeracy
Solving Problems Year 3
© A & C Black 2000

Obstacle course

- **Write the answers and the number statements.**

1. The fence is 76 cm high. The wall is 18 cm higher. How high is the wall? <u>94 cm   76 + 18 = 94</u>

2. Sam is 126 cm tall. Sarah is 19 cm shorter. How tall is Sarah? _____

3. A piece of pipe is ½ m long. Ten pipes are joined together to make a tunnel. How long is the tunnel?

_____

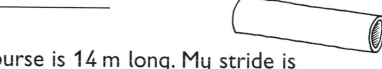

4. The obstacle course is 14 m long. My stride is ½ m long. How many strides will it take me to cross it? _____

5. In the sandpit Ellie jumps 108 cm and Ben jumps 95 cm. How much further does Ellie jump?

_____

6. A rosette is made from a piece of ribbon 20 cm long. How many rosettes can be made from a 3 m length of ribbon? _____

Now try this!

Ben and Ellie jump the sandpit again, but this time Ben jumps | 24 cm further | **than Ellie.**
- **How far could they each have jumped?**

Teachers' note The children will need to think carefully about which number operation to use. Modelling the situation using a metre stick can help them to visualise what is required. In the extension activity, encourage the children to generate a variety of distances.

Developing Numeracy
Solving Problems Year 3
© A & C Black 2000

On the map

- **Look at this map of the places near Jo's home.**

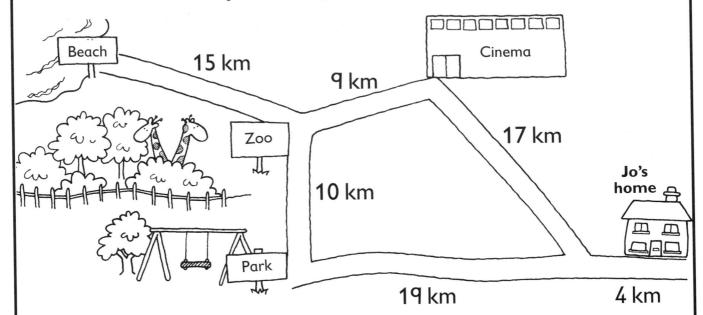

Beach
15 km
9 km
Cinema
17 km
Zoo
10 km
Jo's home
Park
19 km
4 km

1. Find the shortest way to the beach from Jo's home.
   How far is it? _____

2. How much further is the other way? _____

3. If Jo leaves the beach and drives 24 km, which place
   does she visit? _____

4. If Jo leaves her home and drives 30 km, which place does
   she visit? _____

5. Jo uses the shortest way to go to the park and back.
   How far does she drive? _____

Now try this!

**Jo sets off from home, visits all the places on
the map and returns home.**

- **Write the places she visits in order.**
- **What is the total distance she drives?**

Teachers' note In the extension activity, the children may not realise that in order to visit each
place on the map they will have to add one length of road twice. Point out that there is more
than one route.

Developing Numeracy
Solving Problems Year 3
© A & C Black 2000

- **Write the answers and the number statements.**

1. How far will 5 canes stretch?

<u>250 cm</u>   5 × 50 = 250

2. How many canes will stretch 10 m?

_____

3. I buy two pieces of wood. One is

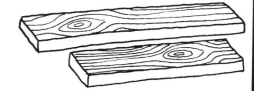

85 cm long, the other is 62 cm long.

What is their total length? _____

What is the difference in length? _____

4. I buy 9 m of washing line to stretch

across my garden. When I get home I

realise I have 3 m more than I need. How

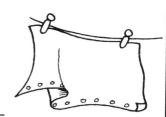

wide is my garden? _____

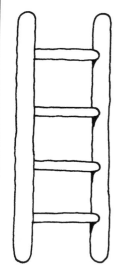

5. I buy 2 ladders. Their total length is 8 m. How long

could each ladder be? _____

6. A brick is 20 cm long. A nail is 4 cm long.

How many nails will stretch as far as

10 bricks? _____

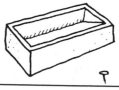

- **Which was the most difficult question to work out? Why?**
- **Which was the easiest? Why?**

Teachers' note Before beginning this activity, the children will need to be reminded of the number of centimetres in a metre and the abbreviations used on the sheet. They could be asked to generate a variety of lengths for question 5. In the extension activity, encourage the children to discuss why they thought some questions were harder than others.

Developing Numeracy
Solving Problems Year 3
© A & C Black 2000

Kitchen quiz

Ryan is working in the kitchen with his gran.

• Help Ryan to answer Gran's questions.

1. If an egg weighs 50 g, what will 6 eggs weigh?

2. How many eggs will weigh 450 g?

3. If a sack holds 4 kg of flour, how much flour will 5 sacks hold?

4. How many sacks will we need for 32 kg of flour?

5. If 8 apples balance 5 potatoes, how many apples will balance 10 potatoes?

6. If 6 bananas balance 10 oranges, how many bananas will balance 40 oranges?

Now try this!

• **Make up three questions which have an answer of** 10 kg .

Example: A bag of potatoes weighs 2 kg. How much will 5 bags weigh?

Teachers' note Before beginning this activity, remind the children that 'kg' stands for 'kilograms' and 'g' stands for 'grams'.

Developing Numeracy
Solving Problems Year 3
© A & C Black 2000

Builders' puzzles

- **Write the answer on the roof of each house.**

1. *40 kg*

   A bucketful of sand weighs 8 kg. How much do 5 bucketfuls weigh?

2. Three bags of soil weigh 5 kg, 7 kg and 19 kg. How much more than 30 kg do they weigh altogether?

3. A brick weighs $\frac{1}{2}$ kg. How much do 10 bricks weigh?

4. A plank of wood weighs 2 kg. How many 1 kg weights will balance 4 planks?

5. There are 20 kg of tiles in a box. There are 10 tiles in the box. What does each tile weigh?

6. A tap weighs $\frac{1}{4}$ kg. What will 10 taps weigh?

7. A bag of sand weighs 5 kg. How much less than 16 kg do 3 bags weigh?

8. Three piles of soil weigh 9 kg, 15 kg and 21 kg. How much do they weigh in total?

Now try this!

- **Which was the most difficult question to work out? Why?**
- **Which was the easiest? Why?**

Teachers' note Before beginning this activity, remind the children that 'kg' stands for 'kilograms'. In the extension activity, encourage the children to discuss why they thought some questions were harder than others.

Developing Numeracy
Solving Problems Year 3
© A & C Black 2000

Let's play cards

- **Cut out the cards and put them face down.**
- **With a partner, take turns to pick one and answer it.**
- **Ask your partner to check your answer.**

1. Katie weighs 12 kg more than Megan. Megan weighs 32 kg. How much does Katie weigh?

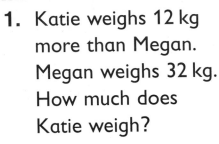

2. 10 plums weigh 650 g. What does one plum weigh?

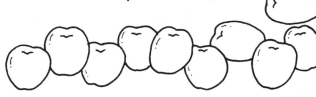

3.  A woman weighs 45 kg. Her brother weighs 60 kg. How much lighter is the woman?

4. An apple weighs 150 g. How much will 5 apples weigh?

5. A large potato weighs $\frac{1}{4}$ kg. What will 8 large potatoes weigh?

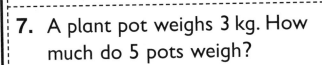

6. Molly weighs 15 kg less than Jack. Molly weighs 26 kg. How much does Jack weigh?

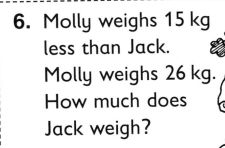

7. A plant pot weighs 3 kg. How much do 5 pots weigh?

8. A bag of onions weighs 8 kg. A cook uses half of them. What weight is left?

9.  A bag of carrots weighs 12 kg. Dad uses 4 kg of them. What weight is left?

10. A bag of sugar weighs 2 kg. There are 24 kg of sugar on a shelf. How many bags are there?

Teachers' note The children should be encouraged to explain their reasoning to a partner. They could be asked to write the answers on the back of the cards. The children could also make up their own cards for other pairs to solve. This sheet can be used as a flexible resource by masking the quantities and inserting more difficult or easier quantities.

Developing Numeracy
Solving Problems Year 3
© A & C Black 2000

It's party time!

At Emma's birthday party, each cup holds $\frac{1}{2}$ litre .

- **Help Emma to answer these questions.**

1. How many cups of lemonade can we pour from the bottle? ☐

2. How many more cups of orange than cups of cola can we pour? ☐

3. How many cups of drink are there altogether? ☐

4. How many people can come to the party if they each have two cups? ☐

5. How many people can come to the party if they each have three cups? ☐

6. If three people are at the party, how many cups can they each have? ☐

- **Make up three questions which have an answer of** 5 litres .

> Example: 10 litres of cherryade are shared equally between 2 people. How much do they each have?

Teachers' note The children should be encouraged to explain their reasoning to a partner.

Developing Numeracy
Solving Problems Year 3
© A & C Black 2000

Computer challenge

- ## Colour the correct answer on each computer.

1.

My kettle holds 2 litres. My teapot holds half as much. How much does my teapot hold?

4 litres	2 litres
$\frac{1}{2}$ litre	1 litre

2.

A bath holds 200 litres. A bucket holds 10 litres. How many bucketfuls will fill the bath?

20	100
50	2000

3.

My pan holds twice as much as my jug. My jug holds $1\frac{1}{2}$ litres. How much does my pan hold?

3 litres	40 litres
9 litres	10 litres

4.

A jug holds 5 cups of water. How many cups of water do 4 jugs hold?

9	20
1	16

5.

I use 30 litres of water to water 10 plants. How much water will I use on 5 plants?

15 litres	40 litres
45 litres	50 litres

6.

I have 40 litres of water. Each flower needs 4 litres of water. How many flowers can I water?

44	22
36	10

7.

A mug holds twice as much as a cup. How many mugs hold the same as 16 cups?

2	8
32	14

8.

A glass holds three times as much as a cup. How many cups hold the same as 10 glasses?

30	3
10	20

- ## Make up three more questions, each with one correct answer and three wrong answers.
- ## Give them to a friend to solve.

Teachers' note The children will need to think about each question carefully as many of the incorrect answers look inviting. Discussion between pairs of children is useful here.

Developing Numeracy
Solving Problems Year 3
© A & C Black 2000

Puzzling capacities

- **Solve these problems with a partner.**

1. A teaspoon holds 5 ml. I put 20 teaspoons of syrup into a cake. How many millilitres is this?

100 ml

2. A medicine bottle holds 45 ml. A teaspoon holds 5 ml. How many teaspoons of medicine in the bottle?

3. A soup bowl holds $\frac{1}{2}$ l. Gran has made 6 l of soup. How many bowls can she fill?

4. A bath holds 50 l of water. A bucket holds 10 l. How many bucketfuls will fill the bath?

5. A bowl holds 10 l of water. How many bowls must I fill to pour 250 l of water into a pond?

6. A soup bowl holds $\frac{1}{2}$ l. The cafe makes 16 full bowls of soup. How many litres is this?

7. A yoghurt pot holds 200 ml. How many pots are needed for 2 l of yoghurt?

8. Mira pours 40 ml of juice into a cup and adds 150 ml of water. How many millilitres of drink does she have?

9. A can holds 300 ml of cola. Sam has 10 cans in the fridge. How many litres of cola does he have?

Teachers' note Remind the children that 'ml' stands for 'millilitres' and 'l' stands for 'litres'. The children should be encouraged to explain their reasoning to a partner.

Developing Numeracy
Solving Problems Year 3
© A & C Black 2000

59

Time for tea

- **Read the times that Danica had a cup of tea on Monday.**

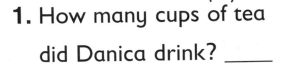

Tea-times on Monday

1 Seven o'clock
2 7·30 a.m.
3 Ten o'clock
4 12·15 p.m.
5 3·20 p.m.
6 5·45 p.m.
7 Nine o'clock at night

1. How many cups of tea did Danica drink? _____

2. How many minutes were there between her first cup and her second cup?

_____

3. How long was it between her

  (a) second cup and her third cup? _____

  (b) third cup and her fourth cup? _____

  (c) fourth cup and her fifth cup? _____

  (d) fifth cup and her sixth cup? _____

  (e) sixth cup and her last cup? _____

4. On Tuesday morning, Danica had her first cup at the same time as on Monday. How long was it between her last cup on Monday and this one? _____

- **Make up the times Danica had tea on Tuesday.**
- **Answer questions 1 to 3 for these times.**

Teachers' note Times can be altered before photocopying to simplify this sheet, for example times can all be presented in digital form, or all in words. You may wish to provide the children with small clocks to assist them with this activity.

Developing Numeracy
Solving Problems Year 3
© A & C Black 2000

Time for tea

- **Read the times that Danica had a cup of tea on Thursday.**

Tea-times on Thursday

1 Quarter to seven
2 7·45 a.m.
3 Quarter past ten
4 12·45 p.m.
5 1·40 p.m.
6 5·55 p.m.
7 Nine o'clock at night

1. How many cups of tea did Danica drink? ____

2. How many minutes were there between her first cup and her second cup?

_____

3. How long was it between her

(a) second cup and her third cup? _____

(b) third cup and her fourth cup? _____

(c) fourth cup and her fifth cup? _____

(d) fifth cup and her sixth cup? _____

(e) sixth cup and her last cup? _____

4. On Friday morning, Danica had her first cup at the same time as on Thursday. How long was it between her last cup on Thursday and this one? _____

Now try this!

- **Make up the times Danica had tea on Friday.**
- **Answer questions 1 to 3 for these times.**

Teachers' note Times can be altered before photocopying to simplify this sheet, for example times can all be presented in digital form, or all in words. You may wish to provide the children with small clocks to assist them with this activity.

**Developing Numeracy
Solving Problems Year 3
© A & C Black 2000**

Cooking trail

- **Follow the trail and answer the cooking questions.**

START

Cake into oven at 10·00. Takes 40 mins. Take cake out at ___10·40___.

Loaf takes 40 mins. Put in at _____. Take out at 8.40.

Sponge cake takes 40 mins. Put in at 3·30. Take out at _____.

Chicken takes 1 hour 20 mins. Put in at _____. Take out at 1·30.

Biscuits take 45 mins. Put in at 11·55. Take out at _____.

Casserole takes _____. Put in at 5·45. Take out at 7·15.

Fruit buns take 20 mins. Put in at 3·20. Take out at _____.

Cheese flan takes _____. Put in at 4·25. Take out at 5·05.

Vegetable pie takes 55 mins. Put in at _____. Take out at 7·00.

FINISH

Roast potatoes take 45 mins. Put in at 7·25. Take out at _____.

Oven chips take 25 mins. Put in at _____. Take out at 5·30.

Meringues take _____. Put in at 5·50. Take out at 7·20.

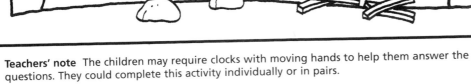

Teachers' note The children may require clocks with moving hands to help them answer the questions. They could complete this activity individually or in pairs.

Developing Numeracy
Solving Problems Year 3
© A & C Black 2000

p 6
1. $100 + 200 = 300$
2. $6 + 2 = 8$
3. $50p - 22p = 28p$
4. $90p \div 6 = 15p$
5. $4 \times 3 = 12$
6. $5 \times 11 = 55$

p 8
1. 5×4
2. $40 \div 5$
3. $8 + 5$
4. 4×12
5. $40 - 12$
6. $12 \div 4$

p 9
1. $+$
2. $-$
3. $-$
4. $\times$
5. $\times$
6. $\div$
7. $+$
8. $\div$
9. $-$
10. $\div$
11. $-$
12. $\div$

Now try this!
$2 + 2 = 4$, $2 \times 2 = 4$, $4 - 2 = 2$, $4 \div 2 = 2$

p 10
1. 19
2. 16
3. 26
4. 7
5. 9
6. 2
7. 5
8. 11
9. 18
10. 32
11. 4
12. 36

p 11
1. 85
2. 183
3. 34
4. 89
5. 51
6. 72
7. 5

p 12
1. 14
2. 19
3. 26
4. 76
5. 228
6. 252
7. 9
8. 46
9. 27
10. 45
11. 88

p 13
1. 10
2. 35
3. 12
4. 24
5. 45
6. 36
7. 3
8. 8
9. 3
10. 8
11. 5

p 14
1. 7 different totals: 11, 9, 15, 6, 10, 7, 12
2. 6
3. 15
4. $9 = 5 + 1 + 3$ $10 = 5 + 3 + 2$
   $7 = 4 + 1 + 2$ $12 = 5 + 1 + 6$

p 15
1. 9 different totals: 15, 11, 21, 17, 18, 19, 16, 12, 20
2. 11
3. 21
4. $16 = 4 + 5 + 1 + 6$ $12 = 2 + 4 + 3 + 3$
   $18 = 6 + 3 + 7 + 2$ $15 = 4 + 4 + 5 + 2$
   $19 = 1 + 6 + 5 + 7$ and $4 + 6 + 3 + 6$

p 16
Multiples of 10 have 0 as a units digit.
Multiples of 5 have 0 or 5 as a units digit.
Multiples of 2 have units digits which follow the repeating sequence 2, 4, 6, 8, 0, 2, 4, 6, 8, 0...
The units digits of multiples of 4 follow the repeating sequence 4, 8, 2, 6, 0, 4, 8, 2, 6, 0...

Now try this!
The units digits of the first doubling sequence follow the repeating sequence 2, 4, 8, 6, 2, 4, 8, 6...
The units digits of the second doubling sequence follow the repeating sequence 6, 2, 4, 8, 6, 2, 4, 8...

p 17
All the totals are possible.

Now try this!
A further special number card showing 32 allows all the numbers to 63 to be formed.

p 18

counters	ways	solutions
7	3	1 + 6, 3 + 4, 5 + 2
9	4	1 + 8, 3 + 6, 5 + 4, 7 + 2
11	5	1 + 10, 3 + 8, 5 + 6, 7 + 4, 9 + 2
13	6	1 + 12, 3 + 10, 5 + 8, 7 + 6, 9 + 4, 11 + 2

Now try this!
The number of ways goes up in ones.
For 21 counters there are 10 ways.

p 19

counters	ways	solutions			
7	3	1 + 2 + 4,	1 + 4 + 2,	3 + 2 + 2	
8	6	1 + 2 + 5,	1 + 4 + 3,	3 + 2 + 3,	3 + 4 + 1,
		1 + 6 + 1,	5 + 2 + 1		
9	6	1 + 2 + 6,	1 + 4 + 4,	3 + 2 + 4,	3 + 4 + 2,
		1 + 6 + 2,	5 + 2 + 2		
10	10	1 + 2 + 7,	1 + 4 + 5,	3 + 2 + 5,	3 + 4 + 3,
		1 + 6 + 3,	5 + 2 + 3,	1 + 8 + 1,	3 + 6 + 1,
		5 + 4 + 1,	7 + 2 + 1		

Now try this!
For 11 counters there are also 10 ways.
For information: this number of ways follows the pattern of triangular numbers: 1, 3, 6, 10, 15, 21..., but each triangular number is repeated. Triangular numbers can be arranged as dots in the shape of a triangle, e.g. •

p 20 and p 21
Children should explore the different possibilities for each total between 0 and 9.
The number of different ways of scoring each total is as follows:

total	ways						
0	1	0,0,0					
1	3	1,0,0	0,1,0	0,0,1			
2	6	2,0,0	0,2,0	0,0,2	1,1,0	1,0,1	0,1,1
3	10	3,0,0	0,3,0	0,0,3	1,2,0	1,0,2	2,0,1	2,1,0
		0,1,2	0,2,1	1,1,1				
4	12	1,2,1	1,1,2	2,1,1	2,2,0	0,2,2	2,0,2	1,3,0
		0,3,1	3,0,1	1,0,3	0,1,3	3,1,0		
5	12	1,2,2	2,1,2	2,2,1	0,3,2	0,2,3	2,3,0	2,0,3
		3,0,2	3,2,0	1,1,3	1,3,1	3,1,1		
6	10	3,3,0	3,0,3	0,3,3	1,3,2	1,2,3	3,2,1	3,1,2
		2,1,3	2,3,1	2,2,2				
7	6	3,3,1	3,1,3	1,3,3	2,2,3	2,3,2	3,2,2
8	3	3,3,2	2,3,3	3,2,3			
9	1	3,3,3					

Children should, therefore, appreciate that it is better to choose a total of 4 or 5 than 0 or 9 as there are more possibilities of this being the resulting total.

p 22 and p 23
Now try this!
Page 22 – possible; page 23 – not possible

p 24
Children may notice that any start number subtracted in this way very quickly falls into the same chain of subtractions of numbers. These numbers are all multiples of 9.
e.g.
$75 - 57 = 18 \rightarrow 81 - 18 = 63 \rightarrow 63 - 36 = 27 \rightarrow 72 - 27 = 45 \rightarrow 54 - 45 = 9$
$64 - 46 = 18$
or $92 - 29 = 63$
or $74 - 47 = 27$ etc.

When children have organised the start numbers into groups with 1, 2, 3, 4 or 5 subtractions to reach 9, they might notice that:
• where 1 subtraction is needed to reach 9, the start numbers have digits with a difference of 1 or 0;
• where 2 subtractions are needed to reach 9, the start numbers have digits with a difference of 5 or 6;
• where 3 subtractions are needed to reach 9, the start numbers have digits with a difference of 3 or 8;
• where 4 subtractions are needed to reach 9, the start numbers have digits with a difference of 4 or 7;
• where 5 subtractions are needed to reach 9, the start numbers have digits with a difference of 2 or 9;
• digits in the answers always add up to 9.

p 26
1. True
2. True
3. True
4. True
5. True

Now try this!
The statement is not always true since a fraction can be considered a number. Suggest that the statement would be more accurate if it referred to whole numbers.

p 27
1. Odd
2. Even
3. Even
4. Even

Now try this!
False. It is possible to get an odd number, but it is also possible to get an even number, e.g. 20 halved = 10. Therefore this is not always true.

p 28
There are many solutions (120!).

p 29
Cube = 6 faces, sphere = 1 face, cylinder = 3 faces, square-based pyramid = 5 faces, cone = 2 faces, triangular prism = 5 faces, cuboid = 6 faces, hemisphere = 2 faces.
The cube, cone, cuboid and hemisphere should be coloured.
Combinations of shapes with 24 faces include:
4 cubes   4 cuboids
2 cuboids and 2 cubes   12 cones
12 hemispheres   1 cone and 11 hemispheres
1 cone, 1 cube, 2 hemispheres and 2 cuboids
3 cones, 1 cube, 3 hemispheres and 1 cuboid   etc.

p 30
1. to 4. There are many solutions.
5. The shortest route is 3 hops.
6. Visiting each pad once, there are several different ways including:

or or

p 32
1.   2.   3.   4. to 6.

square   rectangle   hexagon   octagons

p 33
1. to 3.   4. and 5.   6.

hexagons   octagons   quadrilateral

p 34
False. There are other types of quadrilateral.
False. 3-sided shapes are called triangles.
True
False. 5-sided shapes are called pentagons.

p 35
1. Rectangle and triangle   2. Semi-circle
3. Triangle   4. Pentagon and hexagon:

5. Quadrilateral
Now try this!
Rectangles folded in half can make squares, rectangles or triangles.

p 37
1. 9   2. 17   3. 15   4. 28   5. 11   6. 9

p 38
1. 12   2. 15   3. 13   4. 9   5. 17
6. to 8. There are various answers.

p 39
1. 12   2. 15   3. 11   4. 19   5. 29   6. 26
7. and 8. There are various answers.

p 40
Coloured tables: 1, 3, 4, 5 and 6

p 41
1. 37   2. 49   3. 35   4. 52   5. 40
Now try this!
36, 72

p 42
1. 53   2. 42   3. 5   4. 30   5. 10   6. 24

p 43
1. 7, 6   2. 7   3. 32   4. 8   5. 11

p 44
1. 5   2. Change = £3.50, £0.80, £3.00 and £3.15   3. 10   4. £3.60

p 45
1. 20   2. Change = £3.50, £1.35 and £0.95   3. £7.05   4. £7.00   5. £8.20
Now try this!
Big Dipper twice and Dodgems three times

p 46
1. to 4. Check children's answers.   5. 20p, 5p, 2p, 2p
6. 50p, 20p, 20p, 5p, 2p
Now try this!
46p = 20p, 20p, 5p, 1p   £2.98 = £2, 50p, 20p, 20p, 5p, 2p, 1p

p 48
1. £3.20   2. £3.15   3. Fries and milkshake
4. Salad, fries and cola **or** burger, fries and milkshake
5. Pizza **or** salad and burger

p 49
1. £7.00   2. £1.00   3. Ghost Train and Helter Skelter
4. £2.45   5. £1.35   6. £1.30
Now try this!
Candy floss = 11, Toffee apples = 7

p 50
1. 80p, £1.00, £2.00, 60p, £1.20, £2.80
2. 2 adults **or** 4 children **or** 1 adult and 2 children
3. 2 adults and 1 child **or** 5 children **or** 1 adult and 3 children
4. 10 children
Now try this!
e.g. adults 50p, children 20p

p 51
1. 94 cm, 76 + 18 = 94   2. 107 cm, 126 − 19 = 107
3. 5 m, 10 × ½ = 5   4. 28, 14 ÷ ½ = 28
5. 13 cm, 108 − 95 = 13   6. 15, 300 ÷ 20 = 15

p 52
1. 45 km   2. 3 km   3. Cinema   4. Zoo   5. 46 km
Now try this!
e.g. cinema, zoo, beach, park = 93 km

p 53
1. 250 cm, 5 × 50 = 250   2. 20, 1000 ÷ 50 = 20
3. 147 cm, 85 + 62 = 147   23 cm, 85 − 62 = 23
4. 6 m, 9 − 3 = 6   5. e.g. 5 m, 3 m, 5 + 3 = 8
6. 50, 20 ÷ 4 = 5 × 10 = 50 **or** 20 × 10 = 200 ÷ 4 = 50

p 54
1. 300 g   2. 9   3. 20 kg   4. 8   5. 16   6. 24

p 55
1. 40 kg   2. 1 kg   3. 5 kg   4. 8   5. 2 kg   6. 2½ kg
7. 1 kg   8. 45 kg

p 56
1. 44 kg   2. 65 g   3. 15 kg   4. 750 g   5. 2 kg   6. 41 kg
7. 15 kg   8. 4 kg   9. 8 kg   10. 12

p 57
1. 6   2. 2   3. 12   4. 6   5. 4   6. 4

p 58
1. 1 litre   2. 20   3. 3 litres   4. 20   5. 15 litres
6. 10   7. 8   8. 30

p 59
1. 100 ml   2. 9   3. 12   4. 5   5. 25   6. 8 l
7. 10   8. 190 ml   9. 3 l

p 60
1. 7 cups   2. 30 minutes
3. (a) 2½ hours (b) 2 hours 15 mins (c) 3 hours 5 mins
    (d) 2 hours 25 mins (e) 3 hours 15 mins   4. 10 hours

p 61
1. 7 cups   2. 60 minutes
3. (a) 2½ hours   (b) 2½ hours   (c) 55 mins   (d) 4 hours 15 mins
    (e) 3 hours 5 mins   4. 9 hours 45 mins

p 62
Cake: 10·40   Loaf: 8·00   Sponge cake: 4·10
Casserole: 1 hour 30 mins Biscuits: 12·40   Chicken: 12·10
Fruit buns: 3·40   Cheese flan: 40 mins Vegetable pie: 6·05
Meringues: 1 hour 30 mins Oven chips: 5·05   Roast potatoes: 8·10

64